SIMPLE GEOLOGICAL STRUCTU

PREFACE TO FIRST EDITION

The object of this book is to give a series of notes on the elementary but essential principles concerning the reading of simple geological structures and their implications, from a geological map; and a series of illustrative map-exercises fully worked out and explained. One of us (J. I. P.) is responsible for the somewhat special notes 6–9 and for the preparation and exposition of the map-exercises, while the other (J. C.) is responsible for the more general notes 1–5. It must be understood that these notes, particularly notes 1–5, are in a very compressed form. Certain statements in the notes will occur again where they find their application in the map-exercises. A rigorous exclusion of all overlapping has not been attempted.

Directly these elementary principles are understood in simple cases, their further application can be readily appreciated. Beds are rarely of uniform thickness, strikes are rarely straight lines, axes of folding are rarely horizontal, faults rarely occur with no movement in the direction of their strike, and unconformities rarely occur without overlap; but before considering structures which involve usual but complicating features such as these, the study of ideal cases should be mastered.

The graded series of exercise maps already prepared by one of us (J. I. P.), and published by Messrs. Thomas Murby & Co., may be used conveniently as exercises. The present book owes its origin, in fact, to the favourable reception of this series and the consequent suggestion that such a work would be a useful companion to it.

The student is assumed to have a working knowledge of ordinary topographical map-reading. He should thus be familiar with the idea of visualising a map as representing in two dimensions an unevenly curved surface, and with the method of indicating the third dimension by contour lines. The geological map demands in addition the ability to visualise as a solid the country it represents. This is of fundamental importance in all geological map-reading; it must be realised at the beginning and made a natural habit as the study progresses.

It is also assumed that the student can obtain a knowledge of the elements of those geological and geographical processes of erosion, deposition and earth movement which allow the geological history of a region to be inferred from the geological map. The method of reading this history from the facts supplied by the map will be shown, but space does not allow a discussion of the processes involved. It should be emphasised, however, that the study of geological mapping is intimately bound up with the study of physical, structural and stratigraphical geology, and is indeed an excellent introduction to these aspects of the science of the earth.

Surface relief can only be understood by a reference to the occurrence and disposition of the rocks which make up the country; and a relief map, such as an ordinary topographical map nearly always is, requires a geological map for its proper interpretation. For this reason a knowledge of the elements of geological mapping is really essential to any rational study of physical geography.

A map is not completely "read" until all available quantitative information has been found. Simple but exact methods, such as are possible with a contoured map and deliberately idealised rock-structures, are the basis of treatment.

In conclusion, the authors wish to express their indebtedness to Professor W. J. Pugh for several valuable suggestions incorporated in the text.

J. I. P.
J. C.

SIMPLE GEOLOGICAL STRUCTURES

METRIC EDITION

A SERIES OF NOTES AND
MAP EXERCISES

by

JOHN I. PLATT
M.SC.

and

JOHN CHALLINOR
M.A.

Senior Lecturers in Geology (Retired),
University College of Wales, Aberystwyth

LONDON

THOMAS MURBY & CO
40, Museum Street, London WC1A 1LU
(George Allen & Unwin are the proprietors of Thomas Murby & Co.)

FIRST PUBLISHED JUNE,1930
SECOND EDITION JANUARY,1940
THIRD IMPRESSION (SECOND EDITION)1949
REPRINTED 1951
REPRINTED 1954
REPRINTED (THIRD EDITION)..............1956
REPRINTED 1959
REPRINTED 1962
REPRINTED 1964
REPRINTED (FOURTH EDITION) 1968
REPRINTED 1970
REVISED METRIC EDITION....................1974

ISBN 0 04 550020 7

Printed in Great Britain
by Alden & Mowbray Ltd
at the Alden Press, Oxford

CONTENTS

Note 1

THE BEDDING PLANE

MAPS AND SECTIONS

A geological map is one which shows, in the first place, the occurrence and distribution of the rocks at the surface of the ground. Certain facts of observation about them may be shown by conventional signs. The geological map allows the geological structure of the country to be inferred. In its construction it is based on the topographical map.

A geological section shows the rocks in a vertical plane, cut across the map or some portion of it.

The full meaning of geological maps and sections will only become apparent as they are studied.

BEDDING SURFACES AND CONFORMABLE ROCK SERIES

From the point of view of the understanding of geological structures the most important rocks are sedimentary, stratified or bedded rocks. Beds of rock are bounded by *bedding surfaces* which may be horizontal, tilted or bent in any form and direction. In addition to being bounded by bedding surfaces a bed may be considered as being made up of an infinite number of such surfaces.

A series of beds which have been laid down regularly one on the other, and which may be treated as a whole, form a *conformable series*. It follows that the *lower beds are the older*. In such a series the *bedding surfaces are parallel* in the simpler cases with which we are dealing.

Each bedding surface is usually common to two beds of rock, being the top of one and the bottom of the one next above. In the simplest case these surfaces are planes: *bedding planes*.

PROPERTIES OF A BEDDING PLANE

A bedding plane has all the properties of an ordinary plane surface. The *strike* is the direction in which the slope is nil. The *true dip direction* is the direction on the map of maximum slope downwards and is at right angles to the strike. The *true dip amount* is the angle made by the bedding plane with the horizontal in the direction of true dip; that is, it is the maximum angle so made. This may be expressed in degrees or as a gradient (or in any other way).

By "gradient" the tangent of the angle is meant, e.g. a gradient of 1 in 4 (or 1/4) means 1 unit down vertically for 4 along horizontally.

On a map, true dip direction is indicated by an arrow; the amount being given in figures by the side of the arrow. Direction and amount refer to the bedding surface at the point of the arrow. Horizontal bedding is indicated by the sign +, and vertical bedding by the sign ——|——, the longer line (in the latter case) showing the direction of strike.

A *strike line* is a line drawn horizontally on the bedding plane (that is, parallel to the direction of strike). Strike lines are therefore to be considered as contour lines on the bedding plane and there are an infinite number of such lines, but only those are drawn that differ by a certain arbitrary vertical interval as convenient. Strike lines on a map are the projection of these lines on to the horizontal plane of the map. Strike lines for any one bedding plane are straight, parallel and equidistant for the same vertical intervals.

The *apparent dip* in any given direction is the angle made by the bedding plane in that direction with the horizontal.

Apparent dip is always less than the amount of true dip. True dip and strike may be considered as two limiting cases of dip in general; true dip when this is at a maximum and strike when it is at a minimum; while apparent dip applies to any intermediate direction and amount. The nearer the apparent dip direction is taken to the strike, the less will be its amount (that is, the more nearly will it approach zero); and the nearer it is taken to the direction of true dip, the greater will be its amount (that is, the more nearly will it approach the amount of true dip).
The word "dip" without further qualification refers to "true dip".

Thus, strike is a direction and strike lines are selected lines parallel to this direction. True dip is both a direction and amount, and apparent dip may refer to any direction and has a correspondingly varying amount.

THE DETERMINATION OF A BEDDING PLANE

In general, a bedding plane can be completely determined if three points on it (not in a straight line) can be found. In particular, the true dip of a bedding plane can be found if we are given, or can first find, any strike line and in addition one point outside it.

Two examples may be given to illustrate this.

(1) A bedding plane has an apparent dip of 1/3 in a S.E. direction and of 1/4 in a S.W. direction. *Find the direction and amount of dip.*
Suppose the plane of the paper to represent a horizontal plane surface of ground, and the bedding plane to be at the surface, or at some known distance below the surface, at O (fig. 1).
Draw OA in a S.E. direction and OB in a S.W. direction, making OA 3 convenient units in length and OB 4 units.
Below each of the points A and B the bedding plane will be one unit lower than it was at O.

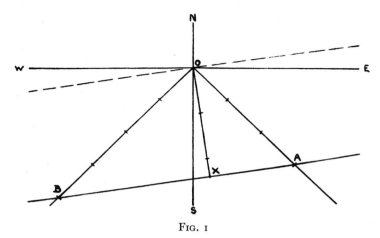

FIG. 1

BA is therefore a strike line, and a line drawn parallel through O is another strike line (it is not necessary to draw this); and the vertical interval between the strike lines is one unit.

Draw OX perpendicular to BA to meet BA in X. OX is the direction of true dip (S., $8\frac{1}{2}°$ E.) and $1/OX$ ($1/2.4$) is the amount.

As an exercise, and to make sure that the diagram is understood, sections to show the surface of the ground and the bedding plane should be drawn along the lines OA, OB and OX.

(2) Three coal pits A, B, C at the corners respectively of an equilateral triangle on a horizontal plane surface of ground enter the same coal seam at 100 m, 200 m, and 400 m respectively below the surface. The side of the triangle is 500 m in length and C is due S. of A. *Find the direction and amount of dip* of the upper surface of the coal seam, supposing this to be a plane surface.

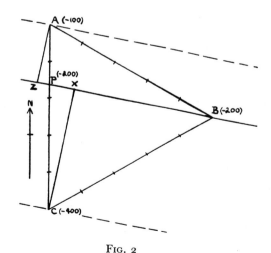

FIG. 2

The depth of the coal seam below B is 200 m.

As the slope of a plane is regular in any direction, the coal seam will also be 200 m below the surface at P (fig. 2) which is one-third of the distance from A to C.

8

BP is therefore a strike line (lines through A and C, parallel to BP, are also significant strike lines).

From C draw CX perpendicular to BP.

XC by its direction and length gives the direction and amount of true dip (S., $11\frac{1}{2}°$ W. and $1/1.65$).

These same values would be obtained by finding a second point 100 m below the surface, to correspond with C. Also, in the above case, AZ, perpendicular to BP produced, would give the same results as XC.

EXERCISES FOR THE STUDENT

Simple exercises similar to the above are given in No. 5 of Platt's Series of Elementary Exercises upon Geological Maps, while Nos. 9a and 9b are more difficult.

OUTCROP

The *outcrop* of a bedding plane is the line of intersection of the bedding plane with the surface of the ground; that is, the line along which the bedding plane emerges at the surface. In a map it is the projection of this line on to the horizontal plane of the map.

Given the outcrop of a bedding plane on a contoured map the plane can be completely determined; usually this determination requires only a small part of the whole outcrop, so that if some portion of the outcrop is given the whole can be completed.

METHOD OF COMPLETING THE OUTCROP ON A MAP

Find two points on the outcrop where it crosses the same contour line.

Draw a line across the map through these points. This is a strike line and the value of the strike line is the same as that of the contour line.

Find any other single point where the outcrop cuts another contour line and draw through this a line parallel to the strike: the value of this second strike line will similarly be that of this second contour line.

Label all strike lines as drawn.

When two strike lines are drawn any others are known; all strike lines drawn at the same vertical interval being equidistant (and parallel).

Draw strike lines to the limits of the map (at the same vertical interval as that of the contour lines; usually 100 m).

Having labelled each strike line and the contour lines being already labelled, mark on the map all points where each strike line cuts its corresponding contour line.

These are points on the outcrop of the bedding plane.

Complete the outcrop by drawing a smooth line through these points.

There are two important rules (the validity of which may be proved as an exercise) to be observed in joining up these points.

(1) The outcrop line can only cut a strike line or a contour line where equal-valued lines (one of each) intersect; that is, it must go through both at once.

An outcrop line must not be taken across any strike line or any contour line except at the proper points of intersection.

(2) The outcrop line must go right through the point into the opposite angle. It is also useful to bear in mind the presence and probable positions of interpolated contour lines and strike lines.

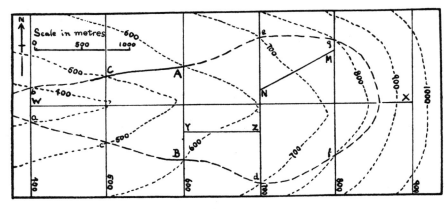

Fig. 3

This procedure is illustrated in fig. 3. Two detached parts of the outcrop of a bedding plane are given (these are shown as continuous lines).

Draw a strike line (the 600 m strike line) through the points A and B.

Draw another (the 500 m) parallel to it through C.

The direction of strike and the horizontal strike interval being known, draw further strike lines to the limits of the map.

Mark the points a, b, c, d, e, f and g and complete the outcrop by continuing through these points the parts already given.

Note that the outcrop of a bedding plane need not be continuous within the limits of the map; and, also, may occur as isolated pieces. The same applies to contour lines which may be considered as the outcrops of horizontal planes. But neither outcrop lines nor contour lines can have any "loose ends".

Note also that, as a bedding plane can be completely determined by knowing the position in space of any three points on it, given any three points where the outcrop cuts any contour lines all the strike lines can be drawn in and the complete outcrop traced. It is merely convenient to choose, if possible, two points on the same contour line to enable the strike to be determined straightaway. Three points on the same contour line will be in the same straight line; this line will be a strike line but will not give the dip.

As shown above, the direction and amount of true dip, and the apparent dip in any direction, can be obtained by measuring distances between two strike lines. Thus in fig. 3 either the line WX or the line YZ, or any other line at right angles to the strike, shows that the dip is 1/8 in a direction due W. The length of the line MN shows that in the direction MN the apparent dip is 1/9.

FACTORS GOVERNING THE FORM OF THE OUTCROP OF A BEDDING PLANE

1. The **direction of strike.** The outcrop tends to follow a strike line.
2. The **relief.** The outcrop tends to follow a contour line.

In general, the degree to which each of these factors influences the form of the outcrop depends on the *amount of dip* and the amounts of the *slopes of the ground*.

When the dip is 0° (bedding plane horizontal) there is no strike (or, rather, any line drawn on the bedding plane is a strike line) and the outcrop is a contour line; it is entirely determined by the relief. When the dip is 90° (bedding plane vertical) the outcrop is entirely determined by the strike and will be a straight line parallel to the strike whatever the relief. Between these two extremes, the strike factor becomes more and more important and the relief factor less and less important as the amount of dip increases.

Similarly, when the ground is a flat horizontal surface, the outcrop is entirely determined by the strike; and the strike factor becomes less and less important, and the relief factor more and more important as the slopes of the ground increase in steepness.

Within the limits of the above controls the actual form of the outcrop depends on the relation between the *direction* of dip and the *direction* of ground slope.

In the case of the strike crossing a river valley more or less at right angles, the outcrop "Vs" either upstream or downstream according to the relation between the direction and amount of dip of the bed on the one hand and the direction and amount of slope of the valley floor on the other; and the angle of the "V" varies also. The effects of this relation on the outcrop may be worked out by taking various cases as the bedding plane passes through an angle of 180°, supposing it to revolve about a horizontal line in it. Significant cases are: bedding plane vertical, dipping upstream, horizontal and three cases of downstream dip when the amount of dip is less than, equal to, and greater than the angle of slope of the valley floor.

For some of these cases, see No. 2 of Platt's Series of Elementary Exercises upon Geological Maps.

Note 2

THE BED

As stated above, the ("solid") bed is bounded by bedding surfaces above and below. In the simplest cases these surfaces are parallel planes, though in nature they are rarely parallel except over short distances.

The figure (fig. 4) is a section of such a bed in the direction of true dip.

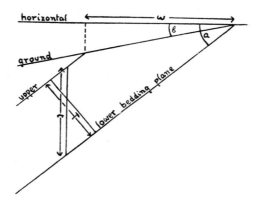

FIG. 4

a—angle of true dip.

b—angle of slope of the ground in the direction of true dip of the bed.

w—*width of outcrop;* the horizontal projection of the distance on the ground between the outcrops of the two planes.

T—*true thickness* of the bed; the perpendicular distance between the two bedding planes.

t—*vertical thickness* of the bed; the vertical distance between the two bedding planes.

Of these, the true thickness is the most fundamental quantity, and secondly the angle of dip. The vertical thickness depends entirely on these two. The width of outcrop depends in addition on the angle of slope of the ground. The ways in which these vary among themselves can be readily seen by making sketch diagrams (as fig. 4) of different cases.

If we are given certain of these values, the rest can be found graphically by "translating" the data into a section-diagram and reading off the other values. When a and t are the two values required a slight construction is necessary.

The vertical thickness of a bed (or, generally, the vertical distance between any two parallel bedding planes) may be obtained from a contoured map by comparing the strike lines for the upper bedding plane with those for the lower bedding plane. If, for instance, it is found that the 400 m strike line for the upper plane coincides on the map with the 300 m strike line for the lower, then the vertical distance between them (that is, the vertical thickness of the bed or beds between the two planes) is 100 m .

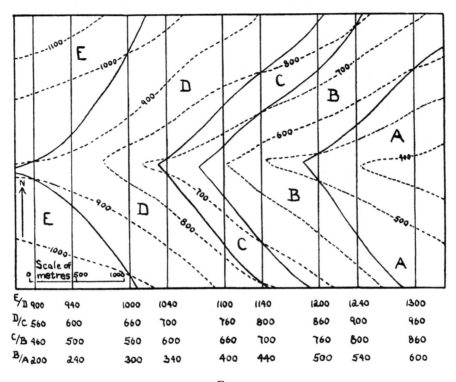

E/D	900	940	1000	1040	1100	1140	1200	1240	1300
D/C	560	600	660	700	760	800	860	900	960
C/B	460	500	560	600	660	700	760	800	860
B/A	200	240	300	340	400	440	500	540	600

Fig. 5

The portion of a map (fig. 5) shows the outcrops of five beds, A, B, C, D and E. The meaning of *outcrop of a bed* follows from that of "outcrop of a bedding plane"; it is the area on the ground, or the projection of this area on to the map, over which the bed appears at the surface.

The vertical thickness of the three beds B, C and D can be determined by comparing the strike lines of the four bedding planes which bound them.

That of bed C (100 m) is apparent at once, as the 700 m strike line for the base coincides with the 800 m strike line for the top.

The 500 m strike line for the base of bed B lies between the 700 m and 800 m strike lines for the top, its exact position coinciding with a line which by interpolation is the 760 m strike line for the top.

The vertical thickness of B is thus 260 m .

Similarly the vertical thickness of bed D is 340 m .

The thicknesses of beds A and E cannot be found because only one bedding plane for each outcrops within the limits of the map.

By tabulating the "labels" for the strike lines of the various bedding planes, the vertical distances between any two of them can be seen at once.

In this case there are two, not four, sets of strike lines because they coincide in pairs.

It is obvious that the strike lines on the bedding planes themselves cannot be coincident, one being 100 m (as usually drawn) vertically below the other, but the projections of these lines on to the horizontal plane of the map may coincide; one strike line on a map may represent any number of strike lines (on the same number of bedding planes) which are in the same vertical plane, and will carry corresponding values. It is therefore important to label strike lines fully. The term "strike line", as also the terms "contour line" and "outcrop line", have therefore two slightly different meanings, one being the line itself and the other the projection of this line on to the horizontal plane of the map.

It follows that, given strike lines on a contoured map for one bedding plane, these strike lines can be made use of in drawing the outcrops of any other bedding planes which are parallel to the first and of known vertical distances apart.

If a second bedding plane is separated from the first by a vertical interval equal to or a multiple of the vertical interval between the strike lines, then the strike lines for the first plane are given new values in drawing the outcrop of the second. If the interval between the two planes is not a simple multiple, then the strike lines for the second plane must be interpolated between those of the first.

The direction and amount of dip of any one bedding plane in a simple conformable series is the same for all other bedding planes. Therefore *in finding the dip of a conformable series confine attention to one bedding plane.*

As an exercise, find the direction and amount of dip of the series A-E in fig. 5.
The fact that a series is conformable should not be taken for granted unless stated; so having obtained the dip of one bedding plane in what is supposed to be a conformable series, this should be checked by seeing that it does actually apply to the other bedding planes also.

FACTORS GOVERNING THE WIDTH OF THE OUTCROP OF A BED

1. The **thickness of the bed.** The thicker the bed the wider the outcrop.
2. The relation between the **dip of the bed** and the **slope of the ground.** The outcrop becomes wider the more nearly the dip of the bed approximates to the slope of the ground.

Note 3

UNCONFORMITY

A block of country may be made up of two or more rock-series which, as regards their structures and other characters, are quite independent of each other. This is clearly shown in section.

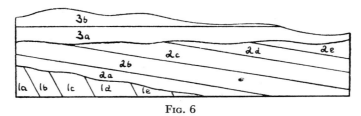

FIG. 6

In the figure (fig. 6) are shown three rock-series, each of the upper two being *unconformable* to the one immediately below. A surface separating two series is a *surface of unconformity*; or, simply, an *unconformity*. In the simplest cases an unconformity may be considered as a surface parallel to the other bedding surfaces of the series of which it forms the base. There is usually no such parallelism, but we are here dealing with an ideal case; and in any case the surface of unconformity will tend to be somewhat uneven.

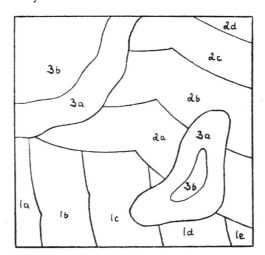

FIG. 7

Unconformity is also clearly shown on a map (e.g. fig. 7, which is not meant to show the same three series shown in fig. 6) by the outcrop of the unconformity cutting across, and hiding (on one side of it) the outcrops of the bedding surfaces of all the lower series. In dealing with a map it is of the first importance to recognise the unconformities. All the beds on one side of the outcrop of the unconformity (until another such outcrop be reached) belong to one series and all on the other side to the other series, remembering that the surface of unconformity itself belongs to the upper series.

The surface of unconformity is the base of the lowest bed of the upper series. It is not the top of any member of the lower series.

Any unconformity will truncate any or all the outcrops of bedding surfaces or unconformities older than itself and will itself be truncated by newer unconformities.

It must be clearly realised that the older series continue underneath the newer.

MAP EXERCISES

In this and the subsequent map exercises in this work the following points should be noticed:

1. The maps are all orientated in the usual way.

2. The altitudes are in all cases given in metres above sea-level.

3. The maps and sections are all drawn to the same scale, viz., 1:40 000.

4. Directions are given in the usual way, e.g. as N., N.W., etc., and as N. 30° W. (i.e. 30° west of north).

5. Strike lines and other lines necessary for the elucidation of the exercises have been drawn.

Map Exercise 1

UNIFORMLY DIPPING ROCK
SERIES AND UNCONFORMITY

[MAP 1]

In the area indicated upon the map there are two rock groups separated by an unconformity which is a plane surface and for which strike lines can be drawn, as shown, proving it to dip at 1 in 20, E. 20° S.

The *upper series* consists of sandstone and limestone, and the bedding plane between them has the same direction and amount of dip as the unconformity, and is therefore parallel to it. Further, the 700 m strike line for the unconformity is coincident with the 800 m strike line for the top of the *sandstone*, proving the latter to be 100 m in vertical thickness (see p. 12). The vertical thickness of the *limestone* cannot be determined as only its base occurs within the area, but the bed attains a vertical thickness of more than 300 m, as indicated in the section.

The *lower series* consists of mudstone, conglomerate, shale and grit. Strike lines drawn for the bedding planes which separate these beds prove them to dip at 1 in 5, W. The vertical thickness of the *grit* cannot be determined, for only its base occurs within the area, but the bed attains a vertical thickness of more than 300 m, as indicated in the section. The 700 m strike line for the top of the *shale* is coincident with the 300 m strike line for the base, the value of the latter being determined by drawing strike lines in the direction of dip at horizontal intervals of 500 metres, from those already drawn upon the outcrop. The vertical thickness of the shale is therefore 400 m. Similarly, the vertical thickness of the *conglomerate* is 600 m. The vertical thickness of the *mudstone* cannot be determined as only the top of the bed occurs within the area, but it attains a vertical thickness of more than 200 m.

NOTES ON DRAWING THE SECTION

The section is drawn along the northern edge of the map.

Draw in pencil the 100 m, 200 m, etc., altitude lines across the section, by joining the points indicated on the end lines of the section.

The method of drawing the section is as follows:

1. Draw the topographical section (the profile) by projecting the points where the contours cross the line of section on to their corresponding altitude lines and then joining the points projected. (These projections are not indicated in the section.)

2. Draw the plane of unconformity by projecting, as before, *the points where the strike lines of this plane cut the line of section* and then joining the points projected.

Map 1

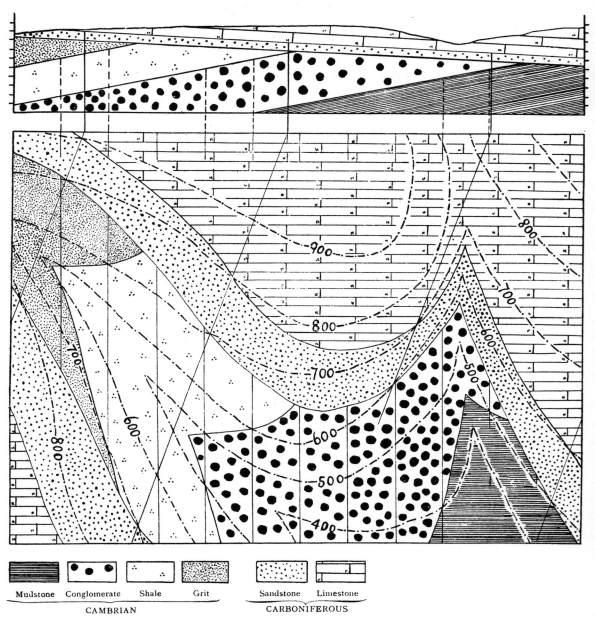

Mudstone Conglomerate Shale Grit Sandstone Limestone

CAMBRIAN   CARBONIFEROUS

The section is drawn along the northern edge of the map.

3. Similarly, draw the base of the limestone by projecting, as before, the points where the strike lines for this plane intersect the line of section and then join the points projected.
4. Similarly, draw, one by one, the bedding planes of the lower series, by continuing the strike lines across the upper series to the line of section and then projecting the points of intersection and joining them as before.

DESCRIPTION OF THE MAP

a. SUCCESSION

Vertical Thickness

Upper Series, Carboniferous.	Limestone	...	...	... > 300 m (newest bed)
	Sandstone	...	...	... 100 m
Lower Series, Cambrian.	Grit	...	...	... > 200 m
	Shale	...	...	... 400 m
	Conglomerate	...	...	600 m
	Mudstone	...	...	> 200 m (oldest bed)

b. STRUCTURE
1. The beds of the *upper series*, the Carboniferous, dip at 1 in 20, E. 20° S.
2. The beds of the *lower series*, the Cambrian, dip at 1 in 5, W.

c. RELATION OF ROCK GROUPS
The Carboniferous rocks rest unconformably upon the Cambrian, the plane of unconformity dipping at 1 in 20, E. 20° S.

d. TOPOGRAPHY AND ITS RELATION TO THE GEOLOGICAL STRUCTURE
The highest land (900 m), which is in the north of the map, is formed of limestone. A river, which flows from N.W. to S.E., has worn through the upper series and established its course upon the lower series. Similarly, a tributary stream flowing from N. to S. has also worn through to the lower series.

e. GEOLOGICAL HISTORY
1. Formation of the lower series under marine conditions in the following order: mudstone to grit.
2. Uplift and tilting, followed by subaerial erosion.
3. Submergence and deposition of the upper series in the following order: sandstone to limestone.
4. Uplift and tilting, followed by subaerial erosion and the development of the present surface features.

EXERCISES FOR THE STUDENT
Describe the geology of the country represented in maps Nos. 1, 2, 3, 6 and 7 in Platt's Series of Elementary Exercises upon Geological Maps, and draw sections along suitable directions across each map.

Map Exercise 2

COMPLETION OF OUTCROPS

[Map 2]

It is often impossible to follow the outcrop of a bedding plane for any great distance. Frequently, part of an area is covered by vegetation and various types of superficial deposits such as alluvium, boulder clay, etc., and then the number of exposures is necessarily limited. Nevertheless, a considerable amount of evidence may be obtained from isolated exposures, stream sections, scarp faces, cliffs, beaches, quarries, pits, mine workings, etc., sufficient to construct a geological map of the area. Corroborative evidence may also be obtained from a close examination of the physical features.

The object of this exercise is to show the method of constructing a map of the solid geology of an area under such circumstances, but the accuracy of such maps depends upon the amount of available evidence and the complexity of the structures. If the evidence is scanty there may be more than one interpretation.

PROBLEM To complete the geological map from the information given.

In map 2a, the clay rests successively upon the grit, the shale and the sandstone, thus indicating an unconformity at the base of the clay. To complete the map, therefore, it will be necessary first to determine the outcrop of the unconformity over the whole area, and to do this the strike and dip of the base of the clay must be found. Two strike lines can be drawn for this bedding surface, viz.: the 500 m strike line in the west of the map and the 400 m strike line, which can be drawn in a parallel direction through the point where the bedding surface crosses the 400 m contour. But the 500 m strike line cuts the 500 m contour again in the east of the area, and a similar intersection occurs upon the 400 m strike line in the centre of the area. The base of the clay, therefore, crops out at these points, and its outcrop can be completed as shown in map 2b. It will be noticed that the outcrop V's up the valley and also sweeps round the spur of the hill on the east of the valley. The position in such cases can be determined by interpolating strike lines and contours at 50 m intervals.

From an examination of the outcrop of this bedding plane it will be seen that in each case three lines intersect at the same point, viz. the contour, the strike line and the outcrop. This is always the case and *it is therefore impossible for the bedding plane to cross either of the other two lines except at their point of intersection.*

Map 2

a.

b.

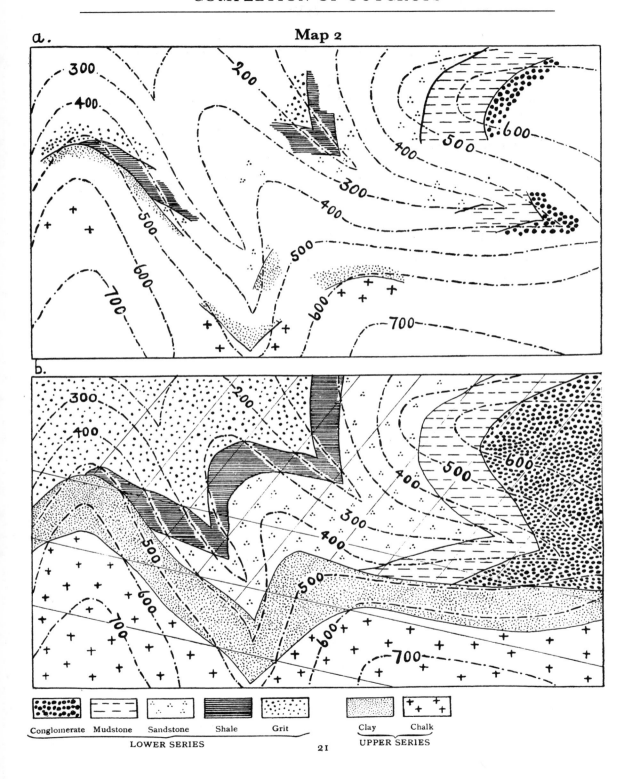

Conglomerate Mudstone Sandstone Shale Grit Clay Chalk

LOWER SERIES

UPPER SERIES

Similarly, the bedding plane between the clay and the chalk can be mapped for the 500 m, and the 600 m strike lines can be drawn for it.

For the remaining beds, a strike line can be drawn for the junction between the grit and the shale at 200 m and others parallel to it at 400 m and 500 m, while one at 300 m can be interpolated. The outcrop of the bedding plane can therefore be completed as before.

Similarly, for the bedding plane between the shale and the sandstone, strike lines at 200 m and 400 m can be drawn, one at 300 m interpolated and the outcrops completed. Also, the outcrop of the bedding planes between the sandstone and the mudstone and between the mudstone and the conglomerate can be completed.

EXERCISES FOR THE STUDENT

1. Describe the geology of the area in map 2b (p. 21).
2. Complete the geological maps in exercises 4 and 8 in Platt's Series of Elementary Exercises and describe the geology of the area represented by each map.

Note 4

FAULTING

A rock series may be broken, or *faulted*, by the forces of earth movement. The fault fracture occurs along a surface which usually approximates to a plane and will be considered as such here. A *fault plane* has a direction and amount of *inclination*, the amount being the angle made with the horizontal; inclination thus being the same property of a plane as dip. (It is convenient to use a different term merely to avoid confusion.) The term *hade* is sometimes used for the angle made by the fault plane with the vertical. All the properties of a bedding plane apply to a fault plane. A fault plane has a direction of *strike* and a line of *outcrop*.

Movement along the fault plane results in any one bedding plane coming to lie in two planes in space, parallel to each other; in one plane on one side of the fault and in the other plane on the other side. This effect of faulting allows certain measurements to be made, of which the most important is the vertical distance between these two planes, the *vertical displacement*, which is the same for all the bedding planes and thus applies to the beds as a whole. The side of the fault on which the beds are lower is the *downthrow side* and the other is the *upthrow side*. A fault is called a *normal fault* when the fault plane inclines to the downthrow side and a *reverse fault* when it inclines to the upthrow side.

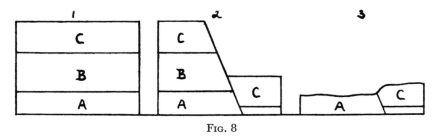

FIG. 8

Although the total movement may be large, the fault grows gradually in many small stages. Usually any cliff or slope, formed on the ground as a direct result of one of these small movements, is soon smoothed off by erosion; and any minor feature formed as a result of faulting is usually caused indirectly by the juxtaposition of rocks of different lithological character along the outcrop of the fault. This is shown in fig. 8, in which bed C is supposed to be more resistant to erosion than beds B and A.

A fault plane is usually a plane of weakness within the rocks, and is thus particularly susceptible to erosion; a groove or valley tending to be formed along the outcrop of the fault plane.

The position of a fault plane may have any relation in space to the positions of the bedding planes. A fault is a *strike fault* when the strike of the fault plane approximates to the strike of the bedding, and a *dip fault* when it approximates to the dip. An *oblique fault* is one in which the strike of the fault plane approximates to neither direction. A fault plane may incline towards, or away from, the direction of dip of the beds; and its inclination may be greater or less than the dip.

A fault is detected on a map by the displacement of the outcrops on the eroded surface of the ground, this being most conspicuous in the case of a dip fault or an oblique fault. A strike fault causes either a repetition or a cutting out of some of the outcrops, the particular effect depending on the relations between the inclination of the fault, the dip of the beds, the slope of the ground, and the side of downthrow. It is instructive to sketch a number of cases and note the effect in each case.

The amount of vertical displacement of the beds, due to a fault, may be found from a map by comparing the strike lines of a bedding plane on one side of the fault with the strike lines of the same bedding plane on the other side. Each series of strike lines will be continued across the fault. Thus, if it is found that the 600 m strike line for the bedding plane on one side of a fault coincides with the 400 m strike line for the same bedding plane on the other side, then the vertical displacement is 200 m . If such ready-made strike lines do not coincide, those that do can be found by interpolation. At any point along the outcrop of a fault plane, the upper rock is on the downthrow side.

We cannot tell, from the resulting geometrical relations in uniformly dipping beds, what actual relative movement has occurred along the fault plane. This may have been simply along the true inclination of the fault; but it may have been along its strike or along some intermediate line, and in these cases the downthrow side, defined as regards the vertical separation of the beds, is not necessarily the side on which there has been relative downward movement.

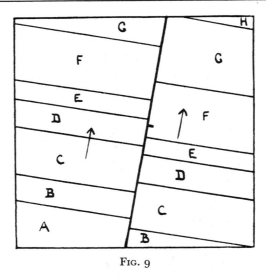

FIG. 9

Fig. 9 is a map of a horizontal surface of ground, showing the outcrops of the several beds in a series faulted by a dip fault. The direction of dip being given, the succession is known and the downthrow side of the fault is thus seen to be on the E. A fault is usually indicated on a map by a thick line, and the downthrow side may be shown by a short line projecting from it at right angles on that side.

SUMMARY OF PROCEDURES FOR FINDING CERTAIN IMPORTANT QUANTITIES FROM A MAP

TO FIND THE DIP OF A BED:

Draw a strike line for one surface.
Draw another strike line for the *same* surface.
Compare the two (measure the distance between).

TO FIND THE VERTICAL THICKNESS OF A BED:

Draw strike lines for one surface.
Draw strike lines for the *other* surface.
Compare the two sets (look for coincidence).

TO FIND THE VERTICAL DISPLACEMENT DUE TO A FAULT:

Draw strike lines for a bedding surface on one side.
Draw strike lines for the *same* surface on the *other* side.
Compare the two sets (look for coincidence).

Map 3

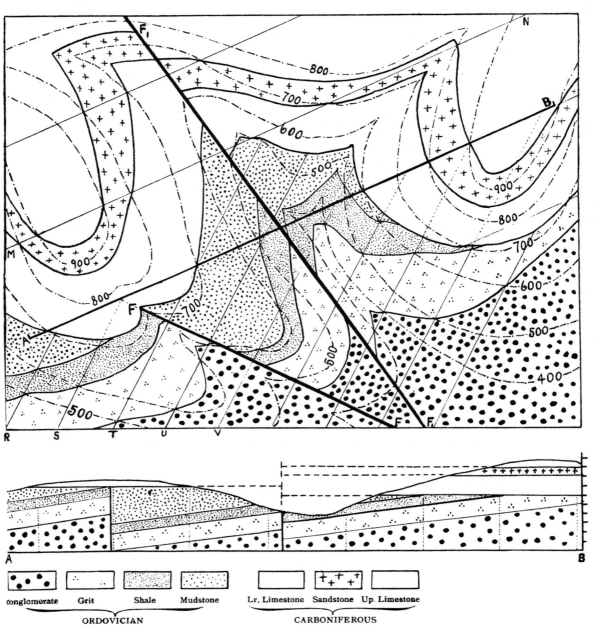

The section is drawn along the line AB.

Map Exercise 3

FAULTING

[Map 3]

In this map there are two series of rocks, an upper series (Carboniferous) and a lower series (Ordovician). These series are separated by an unconformity at the base of the lower limestone. Strike lines for the various bedding planes can be drawn as in map exercise 1, and by means of them the dip of the beds determined.

Two faults, FF and F_1F_1, occur within the area. The one in the S.W., FF, affects the lower series (Ordovician) only and ends on the map at the unconformity, but, in reality, passes beneath the upper series, as do the Ordovician rocks. This fault must have been formed after the youngest Ordovician rocks (the mudstone) and before the deposition of the oldest Carboniferous rocks (the lower limestone), so that its age is post-Ordovician and pre-Carboniferous. Fault F_1F_1, affects both the Ordovician and the Carboniferous rocks and, therefore, its age is post-upper limestone.

TO FIND THE VERTICAL DISPLACEMENT DUE TO THE FAULTS

FAULT FF

Lines R and S are the 600 m and the 700 m strike lines respectively for the top of the shale on the S. side of the fault. Therefore, the lines T, U and V are the 800, 900, and 1,000 m strike lines for the same bedding plane.

But strike line V, when produced across the fault, becomes the 600 m strike line for the same bedding plane; i.e. the 1,000 m strike line on the S. side of the fault is in the same straight line as the 600 m strike line on the N. side of the fault; therefore, the vertical displacement of the beds due to the fault must be equal to the difference between these values, i.e. a displacement of 400 m down on the N. side.

FAULT F_1F_1

Line MN is the 800 m strike line for the base of the sandstone on the S.W. side of the fault, but when continued across the fault it becomes the 700 m strike line for the same bedding plane. Therefore, the fault causes a vertical displacement of 100 m down on the N.E. side.

Similarly, it can be shown that the fault causes the same vertical displacement when it affects the Ordovician series, for the line V is the 500 m strike line for the base of the shale on the S.W. side of the fault and the 400 m strike line on the N.E. side of the fault for the same bedding plane.

THE INCLINATION OF THE FAULTS

Both faults cross the map as straight lines, that is, their outcrop is not modified by changes in topography. Therefore, they are both vertical faults.

THE SECTION

This has been drawn along the strike line AB, and the method of procedure is similar to that followed in exercise 1. As the section line is not along the edge of the map, direct projection is not possible, so that the points where the contours, strike lines, faults, etc., cross the line of section must be transferred by some other means. One method is to transfer each point separately by a pair of dividers, but a quicker method, and one quite as accurate if carefully carried out, is to place a strip of paper, with a straight edge, along the line of section and to mark upon it the points A and B and then any other points which it is necessary to transfer. By placing this paper along the base of the section, with points A and B coincident with the ends, the other points can be marked along the base and then projected upwards to the desired altitude. This method can be used in all cases where direct projection is impossible.

The Method of Drawing this Section is as follows:

1. Draw the profile from the contour lines.
2. Draw the vertical fault F_1F_1. As this fault affects both the upper and lower series, it must be drawn before any beds of these series.
3. Draw the unconformity. As the section is drawn along a strike line for this plane, the latter will be horizontal in the section, and at 700 m on the W. side and 600 m on the E. side of the fault F_1F_1.
4. Draw the beds above the plane of unconformity, *using the strike values to obtain the correct altitudes* (see exercise 1).
5. Draw the vertical fault FF. This does not actually appear along the line of section but it passes beneath the unconformity, affecting only the Ordovician rocks. Nevertheless, the trace of the fault can be marked on the map and the point where this line cuts the line of section can be transferred to the section and the fault drawn vertically downwards from the unconformity.
6. Draw the beds of the lower series. As in the case of fault FF, the trace of some of the strike lines for this series must be continued across the upper series before they intersect the line of section. Similarly, the bedding planes of the lower series will terminate at the unconformity.

When the section is completed, the vertical displacement due to the faults and the thickness of the beds can be checked.

DESCRIPTION OF THE MAP

a. SUCCESSION

				Vertical thickness
Carboniferous	Upper limestone ...	...	...	>100 m (newest bed)
	Sandstone ...	...	...	100 m
	Lower limestone ...	...	...	200 m
Ordovician	Mudstone ...	...	...	>300 m
	Shale ...	...	...	100 m
	Grit ...	...	...	200 m
	Conglomerate ...	...	...	>400 m (oldest bed)

28

b. STRUCTURE

1. The *Carboniferous* beds dip at 1 in 10, N. 26° W.

2. The *Ordovician* beds dip at 1 in 5, W. 27° N.

3. **Faulting.**
Two faults affect the rocks of the area.

   i. Fault F_1F_1: vertical; normal; direction, N. 35° W.; vertical displacement, 100 m down on the N.E. side; age of faulting, post-upper limestone.

   ii. Fault FF: vertical; normal; direction, W. 26° N.; vertical displacement, 400 m down on the N.E. side; age of faulting, post-Ordovician and pre-Carboniferous.

c. RELATION OF ROCK GROUPS

The Carboniferous series rests unconformably upon the Ordovician series and the unconformity is parallel to the dip of the upper series.

d. TOPOGRAPHY AND ITS RELATION TO THE GEOLOGICAL STRUCTURE

A narrow valley crosses the area from N.W. to S.E. and is parallel to, and almost coincident with, the fault F_1F_1, to which it owes its formation. A similar but smaller valley is in process of formation along the line of the other fault, but like the fault, this valley is confined to the Ordovician series, and dies out in the overlying Carboniferous. A third tributary stream in the N.E. flows into the main stream. This has a direction parallel to the strike of the Carboniferous series and is a relic of a drainage system developed in that series. There are no scarp faces, the slope of the land being gentle over the whole of the area.

e. GEOLOGICAL HISTORY

1. Formation of the Ordovician series under marine conditions in the following order: conglomerate to mudstone.
2. Uplift, tilting and faulting (fault FF) followed by subaerial erosion.
3. Submergence and deposition of the Carboniferous series under marine conditions in the following order: lower limestone, sandstone, upper limestone.
4. Uplift, tilting and faulting (fault F_1F_1) followed by subaerial erosion and the development of the present surface features.

EXERCISES FOR THE STUDENT

1. Determine the true thickness of the grit and shale.
2. Describe the geology of the country represented in the exercises 11, 12, 14 and 15 in Platt's Series of Elementary Exercises and Nos. 2 and 3 in Selected Exercises, and draw sections along suitable directions across the maps.

Map 4

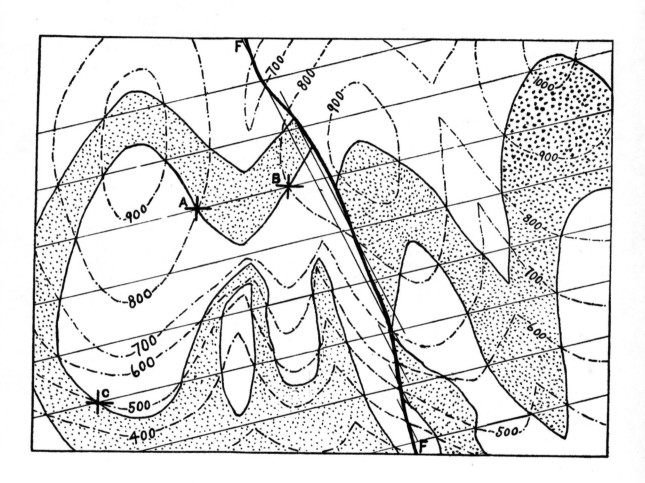

Map Exercise 4

COMPLETION OF OUTCROPS

PROBLEM The upper surface of a bed of sandstone, 100 m in vertical thickness, crops out at points A, B, and C on map 4. FF is a normal fault which causes a vertical displacement of 200 m down on the western side. Assuming the bedding surfaces to be planes, determine the dip of the sandstone and mark in the outcrop of the bed on the map.

[MAP 4]

A. TO MAP IN THE OUTCROP OF THE UPPER SURFACE OF THE SANDSTONE

1. WESTERN SIDE OF THE FAULT

This bedding plane crops out at the points A and B, both of which occur on the 800 m contour line, therefore the 800 m strike line passes through A and B. But conditions are not the same on the eastern side of the fault, therefore the strike lines can only be drawn as far eastward as the fault. Since C is on the 500 m contour, a line drawn through C parallel to the 800 m strike line, will be the 500 m strike line. Interpolate the 600 m and 700 m strike lines and also draw others covering the whole area on the western side of the fault. Write upon each strike line its altitude above sea level. From these strike lines the outcrop of the bedding plane can now be completed as in exercise 2. The outcrop is the continuous line through A, B and C.

2. EASTERN SIDE OF THE FAULT

FF is a normal fault with a vertical displacement of 200 m down on the western side, that is, the rocks on the western side have sunk 200 m without any change in strike and dip taking place. Therefore, if the strike lines already drawn for the upper bedding plane in the western area are continued eastward, they will still be strike lines for the bedding plane but the value of each will be increased by 200 m.

Produce all these lines across the fault and mark upon each its altitude above sea-level. The outcrop of the bedding plane can now be completed as before. The outcrop is the more southerly of the two continuous lines.

B. TO MAP IN THE OUTCROP OF THE BASE OF THE SANDSTONE

The bed of sandstone has a vertical thickness of 100 m, therefore the strike lines already drawn for its upper surface coincide with those for the lower surface but the altitude of each is reduced by 100 m. This applies to both sides of the fault. Using these strike lines, the outcrops of the lower surface can be completed as before by assigning the new value to each strike line and joining the points of intersection with the contour lines. The base of the sandstone is the more northerly continuous line on each side of the fault and on the western side it occurs again in the south-west corner and also as an oval-shaped outcrop in the valley.

Map Exercise 4a

PROBLEM To determine the inclination of the fault in map 4.

Fault FF is a normal fault with a vertical displacement of 200 m down on the western side. It is not vertical, for its outcrop is modified by changes in topography. Let us assume that it is an inclined plane surface, then strike lines can be drawn upon it as upon a bedding plane, and thus its inclination determined. Strike lines can be drawn at 700 m and 800 m . These are parallel and therefore other strike lines can be drawn in the same direction from the points where the fault crosses the 600, 500 and 400 m contours. The interval between these strike lines is constant and from them it can be proved that the fault plane has an inclination of 1 in 1, W. 28° S., that is, at 45°, W. 28° S.

EXERCISES FOR THE STUDENT

Work out exercises 4, 8, 13, 16 and 17 in Platt's Series of Elementary Exercises and Nos. 16, 17 and 18 in Selected Exercises.

Note 5

FOLDING

Rocks may be bent, or *folded*, by the forces of earth movement. In a simple diagrammatic case, folding occurs about an imaginary axial plane within the folded structure, each bedding plane being sharply bent about a horizontal axis of folding or hinge line. The parts on each side are the two *limbs* of the fold. If the dips in each limb are equal in amount the fold is *symmetrical*; otherwise it is *asymmetrical*. A fold in which the dips are inwards is a *syncline* or trough fold, and one in which the dips are outwards is an *anticline* or arch fold. Folding is detected on a map by the repetition of beds, with opposed dips.

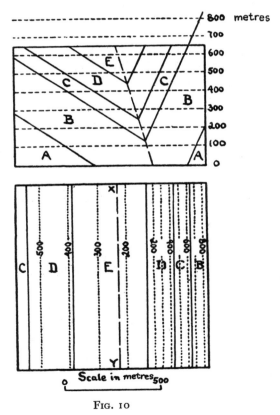

FIG. 10

Fig. 10 shows an asymmetrical syncline of the above type in section and plan, outcropping on a horizontal surface. In the plan (map) the line XY

33

is the outcrop of the imaginary axial plane, and the dotted lines are strike lines for the bedding surface C/B. In the case of a symmetrical fold the strike lines for any surface are the same distances apart in both limbs, or are at least symmetrically disposed (in a curved symmetrical fold). The axial plane is vertical in a symmetrical, and inclined in an asymmetrical fold.

Natural bedding surfaces are bent in a blunt, rather than a sharp angle. In fig. 10 the dips in the limbs are constant. A more usual case in nature is that of curved folding, in which the dips vary in amount in each limb; strike lines will then not be equidistant. Axes of folding (hinge lines) may be inclined to the horizontal; in that case the strike lines on one side of the fold will not be parallel to those on the other side. Folds usually occur as an alternating series of anticlines and synclines.

> As an exercise, variously curved bedding surfaces may be drawn in section and strike lines drawn for them on a corresponding map.
> Note that in finding strike lines for a folded bedding surface, only points on the same side of the axis may be used for finding any one line.

FACTORS GOVERNING THE POSITIONS OF OUTCROP OF THE SEVERAL BEDS IN A CONFORMABLE SERIES

1. **The structure.** Newer beds tend to outcrop as the series is followed in the direction of dip.
2. **The height of the ground.** Newer beds tend to outcrop on the higher ground.

The degree to which each of these factors influences the positions of the outcrops depends on the *amount of dip* and the *differences in the heights of the ground*; the steeper the dip the greater is the importance of the structure factor, and the greater the differences in the heights of the ground the greater the importance of the height factor.

> When the beds are horizontal the positions of the outcrops are entirely determined by the height of the ground; the outcrops of horizontal bedding planes being contour lines.

Thus newer beds tend to outcrop on hills and near the axes of synclines, and older beds in valleys and near the axes of anticlines.

Map 5

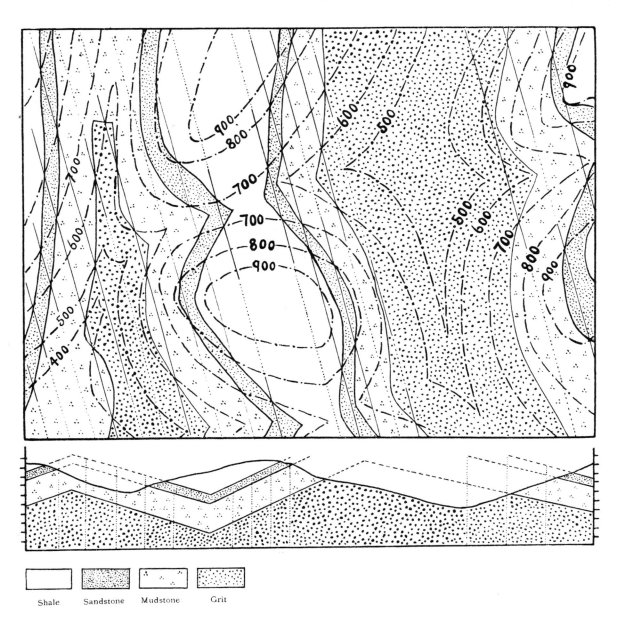

Shale Sandstone Mudstone Grit

The section is drawn along the northern edge of the map.

Map Exercise 5
FOLDING

[MAP 5]

Four beds occur on the map and their outcrops are approximately parallel, suggesting that the beds are conformable. Further, there is a repetition of the outcrops of the same beds, suggesting that the beds are folded and that folding has taken place about axes which trend approximately N.-S.

In order to prove the presence of folding and also the nature of the folds, strike lines must be drawn for the various bedding planes. These lines have been drawn upon the map in a general N.-S. direction and they are all parallel, therefore, they are true strike lines, although what appear to be strike lines can be drawn in a general E.-W. direction, but any such lines are not parallel and, moreover, cannot be strike lines for they are at right angles to the general direction of the outcrops and join points on opposite limbs of the folds. The direction of strike is N. 15° W.

The strike lines prove that the beds are folded into two anticlines separated by a syncline and that the folds are asymmetrical, the dips on the limbs being as follows (reading from W. to E.):

$$(1) \quad \text{1 in } 2\tfrac{1}{2}, \quad \text{W. } 15° \text{ S.}$$
$$(2) \quad \text{1 in 3,} \quad \text{E. } 15° \text{ N.}$$
$$(3) \quad \text{1 in 2,} \quad \text{W. } 15° \text{ S.}$$
$$(4) \quad \text{1 in 4,} \quad \text{E. } 15° \text{ N.}$$

The direction of strike is constant throughout the whole area and is the same as that of the axes of folding. Folding took place after the formation of the newest rocks, the shale, and therefore the age of the folding is post-deposition of the shale.

THE SECTION

This has been drawn along the northern edge of the map and the method of procedure is similar to that followed in previous exercises, a strip of paper being used to transfer the points.

The Method of Drawing the Section is as follows:

1. Draw the profile from the contour lines.
2. Draw the bedding planes upon each limb of the folds from the strike lines.
3. Continue the bedding planes until they meet upon the axes of folding.

N.B.—In this section, the beds are supposed to have a constant dip on each limb and to turn over sharply upon the axes of folding. This, as already stated, is an ideal case. The sections drawn for maps 6, 7, 8 and 9 are nearer approximations to the true nature of folds along the axial planes.

EXERCISES FOR THE STUDENT

Describe the geology of the country represented in exercises 19, 20, 21 and 27 in Platt's Series of Elementary Exercises and Nos. 1, 4, 5, 13 and 15 in Selected Exercises and draw sections along suitable directions across the maps.

Map Exercise 6

MAPS WITHOUT CONTOUR LINES

[MAP 6]

There are no contours included upon this geological map, but the height of the land is given at a few places. As no strike lines can be drawn, it is impossible to determine the structure of the area by this means, but the dip of the beds is given.

In order to appreciate fully the geology of the area we must first study the relief. This is very simple and consists of a valley with high land to the S. and N., the lowest land being in the middle of the eastern edge. This is indicated by the position of the spot-heights, the river and the alluvium. Further, the limestone is the newest rock and as this is horizontal it must occupy all the land above 800 m. Similarly, the clay is horizontal and occupies all the land between 600 and 800 m.

Of the remaining beds, all, except the alluvium, belong to one series, for the outcrops behave in a similar way when crossed by the river. Moreover, the series is folded. This is indicated by the dip arrows and by the repetition of the beds about two parallel lines which trend N.-S. and which coincide with the axes of folding. The eastern fold is an asymmetrical syncline, for the beds on the two limbs dip inwards at different angles. This is indicated by the dip arrows, the V-shaped outcrops when crossed by the river and by the difference in the widths of the outcrops. Similarly, the other fold is an asymmetrical anticline, but the dips of the beds at the surface on the western limb decrease in a westerly direction showing that the dip gradually decreases as the beds pass below the surface.

THE SECTION

The section has been drawn along the northern edge of the map, and has been completed in the following stages:

(1) The profile.
(2) The upper series.
(3) The folded series.

1. THE PROFILE

As there are no contours, the profile cannot be drawn with great accuracy, but several points can be fixed, e.g. the base of the limestone (800 m) and the base of the clay (600 m). The height of the western end is more than 800 m and the eastern end between 600 and 800 m. The region where the sandstone crops out will be lower than 600 m.

37

Map 6

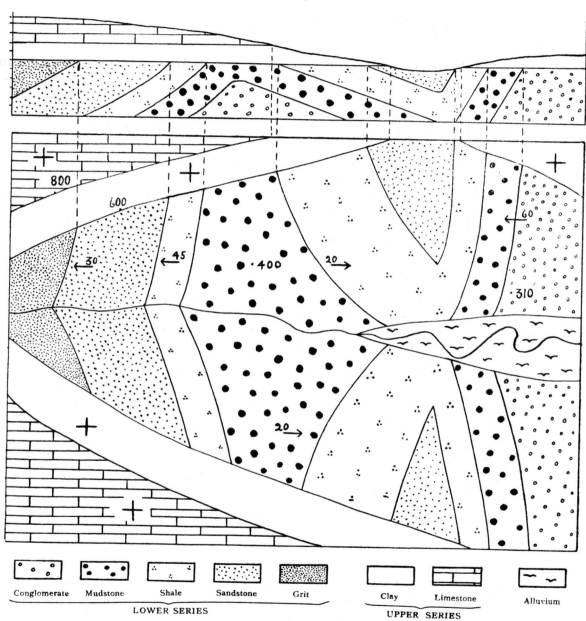

The section is drawn along the northern edge of the map. Spot heights in metres.

2. THE UPPER SERIES

The base of the limestone can be drawn at the 800 m level and the base of the clay at the 600 m level.

3. THE FOLDED SERIES

Only one bedding plane crops out upon the northern edge of the map and this can be indicated in the section by projecting the point of intersection with the section line on to the profile and then setting off a line dipping at 60° W. All the other beds disappear beneath the clay, but the base of the latter is a horizontal plane and also the strike of the beds of the lower series is from N.-S., therefore the outcrops of these beds beneath the clay will still maintain this direction. The bedding planes can be indicated in the section by projecting the points of intersection upon the section line on to the base of the clay and then setting off lines with their respective dips. These lines on the section can only be drawn for short distances at present.

The base of the grit dips at 30° on the western limb of the anticline, while the sandstone, which crops out nearer the axis of folding, dips at 45°. But, these beds are parallel, therefore there must be a change of dip in the sandstone as it proceeds farther away from the axis of folding. This change of dip is shown in the section. The dip of the other bedding planes will also change as they approach the axes of folding until along the axes the beds become horizontal for a short distance. The base of the mudstone and the underlying conglomerate can be indicated in the core of the anticline by determining the true thickness of the mudstone at the eastern end of the section.

DESCRIPTION OF THE MAP

a. SUCCESSION

						Approximate true thickness
	Alluvium					Variable
Upper Series	Limestone	...	...	...	...	>300 m
	Clay ...	...	...	...	...	200 m
	Grit ...	...	...	...	...	>300 m
	Sandstone	...	...	...	...	500 m
Lower Series	Shale ...	...	...	...	...	300 m
	Mudstone ...	...	...	...	...	250 m
	Conglomerate	...	...	...	...	>800 m

The thicknesses are determined by measurement on the section.

The alluvium is the newest rock and the conglomerate the oldest rock.

b. STRUCTURE

1. The *upper series* is horizontal.

2. The *lower series* is folded into an asymmetrical anticline in the centre and an asymmetrical syncline in the east of the area; the dips, reading from

W. to E., are: 30° W., 45° W., 20° E., and 60° W.; the axes of folding are parallel and trend from N.-S.; and the age of the folding is post-grit and pre-clay.

c. RELATION OF ROCK GROUPS

1. The upper series rests unconformably upon the eroded edges of the folded lower series.

2. The alluvium rests unconformably upon the eroded edges of the folded series.

d. TOPOGRAPHY AND ITS RELATION TO GEOLOGICAL STRUCTURE

The area indicated upon the map is that of a valley cut out by a river which flows eastwards through a plateau of horizontally-bedded rocks (limestone and clay), which now form all the land above the 600 m contour. Owing to the folding, the river has had a marked effect upon the outcrops of the bedding planes of the lower series, causing them to V in the direction of dip. In the trough of the syncline, the river has worn through the sandstone and almost through the underlying shale. The course of the river is straight in the west, but where it flows over the alluvium it has developed considerable meanders.

e. SPECIAL POINTS

The alluvium is a thin superficial deposit of recent formation and laid down by the river.

f. GEOLOGICAL HISTORY

1. Formation of the lower series under marine conditions, in the following order: conglomerate to grit.

2. Uplift and folding of the lower series, followed by subaerial erosion.

3. Submergence and deposition of the clay and the limestone.

4. Uplift, erosion, formation of the river valley and the deposition of the alluvium.

EXERCISES FOR THE STUDENT

Work out exercises 24, 26 and 29 in Platt's Series of Elementary Exercises and Nos. 19 to 31 in Selected Exercises. All these latter exercises show igneous rocks in addition. Draw sections across the areas to illustrate the geological structure.

Note 6

IGNEOUS ROCKS

From the point of view of geological mapping and map-reading, the most important characteristics of igneous rocks are their form, and their relation to the rocks in which they occur. Moreover, the subdivision into extrusive and intrusive bodies is of primary importance in this connection as in others.

EXTRUSIVE ROCKS include such types as lavas, ashes, tuffs, volcanic agglomerates, etc. These are usually in the form of *flows* or *beds of pyroclastic material*, which rest upon the eroded land surface; or are interbedded with stratified rocks of the same age. Interbedded flows are known as *sheets*. They are usually of localised occurrence and often show considerable variations in thickness.

Since extrusive rocks rest upon or are interbedded with stratified rocks, the same methods for determining their structural arrangement from an examination of their outcrops can be applied as those already discussed for bedded series.

INTRUSIVE ROCKS vary considerably in form and can be divided into two groups, viz.:

    a. *Those injected along planes of stratification.*
    b. *Those injected across planes of stratification.*

a. BODIES INJECTED ALONG PLANES OF STRATIFICATION

These include sills and laccolites.

Sills are intrusive masses of wide extent and relatively small thickness which are injected usually along bedding planes, but sometimes crossing obliquely from one plane to another, when they are known as *transgressive sills*.

Laccolites are similar to sills, but are much thicker and generally have a dome-shaped upper surface which has arched the overlying rocks. They can be considered as localised sills and their outcrop is often circular in form.

The methods which we have already discussed for determining the structural properties of bedded rocks from their outcrops can, therefore, be applied for sills and laccolites.

b. BODIES INJECTED ACROSS PLANES OF STRATIFICATION

This group includes dykes, bosses and volcanic necks. These bodies cross the country rocks at very steep angles and are often vertical.

Dykes generally approximate to the vertical and have a small thickness compared with their lateral extent.

Volcanic necks are small masses more or less circular in outcrop, being filled-up vents containing volcanic or pyroclastic rocks.

The term *boss* is applied to any large irregular, intrusive body, the sides of which often approximate to the vertical.

In considering this group of intrusive bodies from a point of view of geological mapping, two points are of importance, viz.: the contact of the igneous body with the country rock and the shape of the outcrop. From an examination of these, we are able to determine the form of the intrusion and also the period when the activity occurred (that is, the age of the intrusion). The age of an intrusion must be subsequent to the formation of the country rocks, but if the bodies show a definite association with the structures of the area, such as folding and faulting, the age of the intrusion can be determined with greater accuracy.

Map Exercise 7

IGNEOUS ROCKS

[MAP 7]

Three types of igneous rocks occur within the area; these are dolerite, quartz porphyry and granite, and their names suggest that they are intrusive rocks.

Two outcrops of *dolerite* cross the Ordovician series. Their boundaries are straight lines and they are narrow compared with their length, therefore they are dykes with vertical sides. The western dyke thins out south-westward, but neither is affected by nor associated with the folding of the Ordovician rocks into which they are intruded; further, they end abruptly at the unconformity, therefore the age of intrusion of both is post- the folding of the lower series and pre- the deposition of the upper series.

The *quartz porphyry* forms three separate outcrops within the limestone, and these end abruptly against the faults. Strike lines can be drawn for the junction of the quartz porphyry with the limestone and each portion has the same strike and dip as the limestone. The intrusion is therefore a non-transgressive sill. The sill is affected by the faulting and its age is, therefore, post-formation of the limestone and pre-faulting.

The *granite* forms a circular outcrop, occupies the highest land and is surrounded by limestone into which it has been intruded. There is no evidence, however, that the granite has domed up the limestone, neither is there any evidence that the upper surface of the intrusion is dome-shaped, therefore the intrusion is probably a boss which has approximately vertical sides. Because the granite is intruded into the limestone, its age is post-limestone, but as it is not crossed by the faults, the relative ages of the two cannot be determined.

THE SECTION

This has been drawn along the line AB. The profile, and the sedimentary rocks have been plotted as in previous exercises. The outcrop of the western dolerite dyke has been projected directly on to the profile and drawn as a vertical body. The outcrop of the eastern dyke does not cross the section line but its trace beneath the unconformity is indicated upon the map and its position projected and plotted as before. The dyke is truncated by the unconformity. The quartz porphyry sill, being interbedded with the limestone, has been treated in the same way as a bedded rock. It is indicated in the section by a different symbol. The granite boss has been projected in the same way as the dykes, but the junction with the limestone is indicated as an almost vertical, irregular surface.

43

Map 7

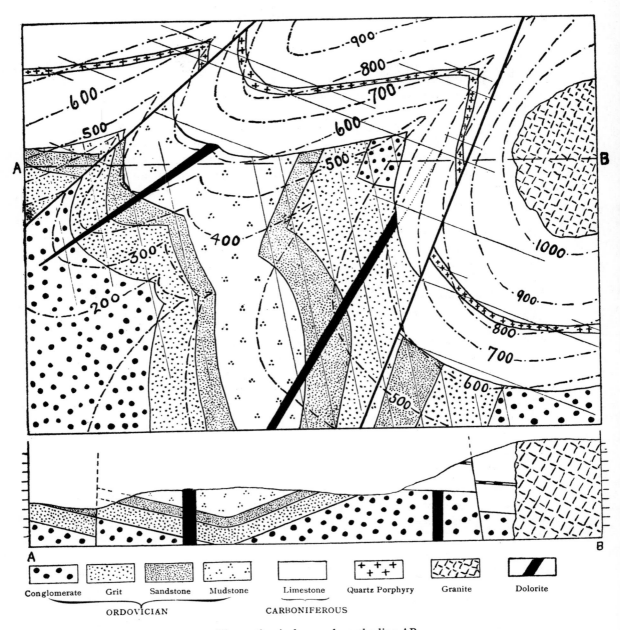

The section is drawn along the line AB.

DESCRIPTION OF THE MAP

a. SUCCESSION

1. Sedimentary Rocks

				Vertical thickness
Carboniferous	Limestone	...	...	>900 m (newest bed)
Ordovician	Mudstone	...	...	>200 m
	Sandstone	...	...	100 m
	Grit ...	...	...	200 m
	Conglomerate		...	>400 m (oldest bed)

2. Igneous Rocks

Granite	...	...	Intrusive.
Quartz porphyry		...	Intrusive.
Dolerite	...	...	Intrusive.

b. STRUCTURE

1. The *Carboniferous* rocks consist of limestone which dips at 1 in 7, N. 22° E.

2. The *Ordovician* rocks are folded into an asymmetrical syncline, the trend of which is N. 10° W. The beds dip at 1 in 4, E. 10° N. in the W. and 1 in 3, W. 10° S., in the E. The age of the folding is post-Ordovician and pre-Carboniferous.

3. *Faulting.* The area is crossed by two faults.

    i. Fault in the N.W.: vertical; normal; direction, E. 42° N.; vertical displacement, 200 m down on N.W. side; age of faulting, post-intrusion of quartz porphyry.

    ii. Fault in the E: vertical; normal; direction, N. 22° E.; vertical displacement, 200 m down on S.E. side; age of faulting, post-intrusion of quartz porphyry.

The region between the two faults is a horst with a vertical displacement of 200 m. Both faults are approximately parallel to the dip of the upper series and were probably caused by the same movement which brought about the uplift and tilting of that series.

c. RELATION OF ROCK GROUPS

There is an unconformity at the base of the limestone, which rock rests upon the lower series.

d. IGNEOUS ROCKS

There are three distinct intrusions in the area.

1. The *dolerite* occurs as two vertical dykes, approximately parallel and with a general N.E. direction. They are intruded into the lower series only and are both of the same age, viz. post-folding and pre-deposition of the limestone. The western dyke thins out in a S.W. direction while the eastern dyke has a uniform thickness of 100 m.

2. The *quartz porphyry* occurs as a non-transgressive sill, 25 m thick, intruded into the limestone at 300 m above its base and having the same direction and amount of dip as the limestone. The age of the intrusion is post-limestone and pre- faulting.

3. The granite crops out in the E. of the area, is probably a boss with approximately vertical sides and its age is post-limestone.

e. TOPOGRAPHY AND ITS RELATION TO THE GEOLOGICAL STRUCTURE

Two streams cross the area flowing approximately from N.E. to S.W., i.e. in the opposite direction to the dip of the limestone. They are, therefore, obsequent streams and as they maintain their direction when crossing the lower series, the drainage in the area occupied by these latter rocks is superimposed. The higher land in the area is occupied by the granite boss which has a comparatively flat top. The other intrusions do not make definite physical features.

f. GEOLOGICAL HISTORY

1. Formation of Ordovician series under marine conditions, from conglomerate to mudstone.

2. Folding and uplift, intrusion of dolerite dykes and erosion.

3. Submergence and deposition of the limestone.

4. Intrusion of the quartz porphyry and the granite.

5. Uplift, tilting and faulting; and wearing out of the present surface features.

N.B.—The intrusion of the granite may have occurred at any time after the formation of the limestone; and the intrusion of the quartz porphyry at any time after the formation of the limestone and before the faulting.

EXERCISES FOR THE STUDENT

Describe the geology of the country shown in exercises 23 and 25 in Platt's Series of Elementary Exercises and most of the maps in Selected Exercises. Some of the maps from No. 20 onwards in Selected Exercises are more difficult as they illustrate pitching folds. Draw sections across each of the maps.

Note 7

SUPERFICIAL DEPOSITS

The two most important superficial deposits are alluvium and boulder clay, while others include blown sand, shingle and sand beaches, raised beaches, river terraces, peat, moraines, etc.

They are all of recent origin, being deposited upon the eroded surface of the solid rocks. *Alluvium* usually occurs along the courses of present-day rivers. It is thus almost invariably the newest rock on a map. *Boulder clay* is found to occur more irregularly than alluvium, but generally upon gentle slopes or flat land.

Rarely do superficial deposits attain any great thickness. In geological sections they appear as unconformable layers and the shape of their lower and upper surfaces depends upon the type of deposit, so that it is necessary to realise their general character and mode of formation to avoid all difficulty.

Alluvium is generally shown on all types of geological maps but on *"solid maps"* other superficial deposits are omitted. *"Drift maps"*, on the other hand, show the position of all superficial deposits and the outcrop of solid rocks where not covered by these deposits.

Map 8

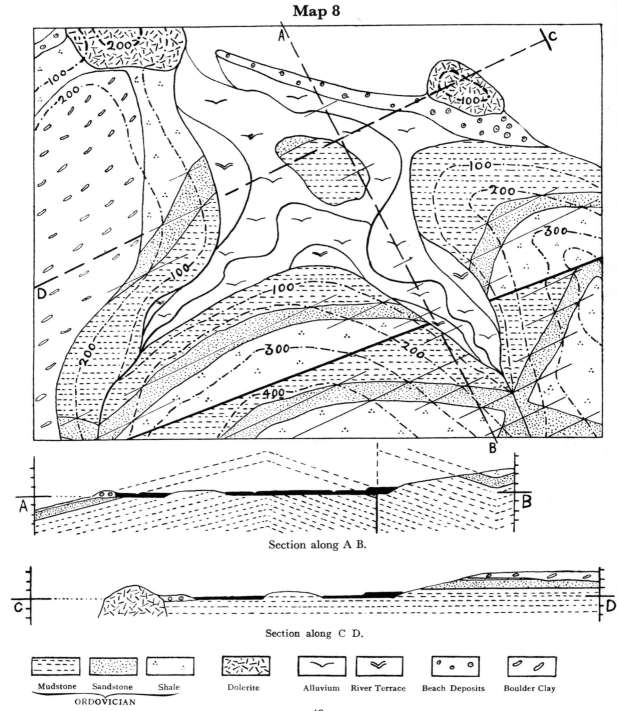

Section along A B.

Section along C D.

| Mudstone | Sandstone | Shale | Dolerite | Alluvium | River Terrace | Beach Deposits | Boulder Clay |

ORDOVICIAN

Map Exercise 8

SUPERFICIAL DEPOSITS

[MAP 8]

The superficial deposits of the area indicated upon map 8 consist of alluvium, river terrace, beach deposits and boulder clay.

THE SECTIONS

These have been drawn parallel to the direction of dip and the direction of strike respectively of the folded series, viz, along lines AB and CD. As the map is of a coastal region and has very low relief, the sections have been continued below sea level. They have been constructed in the following stages:

1. The profile.
2. The dolerite.
3. The superficial deposits.
4. The fault.
5. The Ordovician rocks.

The alluvium and river terrace have been indicated in black upon the sections.

DESCRIPTION OF THE MAP

a. SUCCESSION

1. Sedimentary Rocks

(i.) Superficial deposits *Vertical thickness*

Alluvium	unknown
River terrace	unknown
Beach deposits	unknown
Boulder clay	unknown

(ii.) Ordovician

Shale	>400 m
Sandstone	100 m
Mudstone	>400 m

2. Igneous Rocks

Dolerite	Intrusive

b. STRUCTURE

1. Folding

The Ordovician series is folded into a symmetrical syncline in the S.E. of the area and an asymmetrical anticline in the centre. The folds trend E. 26° N. Passing from S.E. to N.W. the beds dip as follows: 1 in 3, N. 26° W.; 1 in 3, S. 26° E.; 1 in 4, N. 26° W. The age of the folding is post-Ordovician.

2. Faulting

One fault crosses the area, the properties of which are as follows: vertical; normal; direction, E. 22° N., almost parallel to strike of folded series; vertical displacement, 400 m down on N. side; age of faulting, post-Ordovician. Being a strike fault, the faulting and folding probably occurred at the same period.

c. RELATION TO ROCK GROUPS

The superficial deposits rest upon the eroded edges of the lower series.

d. IGNEOUS ROCKS

There are two dolerite intrusions. Because they rise abruptly from the sea and form steep-sided headlands, they are probably small bosses with approximately vertical sides. Age of intrusion is post-folding of Ordovician and pre-formation of beach deposits.

e. SPECIAL POINTS

1. Boulder Clay

This is a glacial deposit which covers the 200 m plateau in the W. of the area. It extends below the 200 m contour on the N. and E. of its outcrop. It has been preserved from denudation by the flat character of the ground.

2. Beach Deposits

These occur in two localities along the coast, in the N. and N.W. of the area. The larger outcrop is in the N. and lies between the dolerite headland and the mainland and also extends westward as a long sand-spit. This westward extension of the sand-spit indicates a movement of tides and currents along the coast from E. to W., deposition of the sand taking place in the calmer waters on the lee-side of the headland. This also applies to the outcrop in the N.W. Further, the westward extension of the sand-spit has caused the mouth of the river to be diverted westward, thus allowing deposition of the alluvium behind it.

3. Alluvium

This fills the lower parts of the river valleys and the region behind the sand-spit, and in the latter region it probably extends below sea-level.

4. River Terrace

A river terrace at approximately 70 m above sea-level forms five separate outcrops along the edge of the alluvial tract.

f. TOPOGRAPHY AND ITS RELATION TO THE GEOLOGICAL STRUCTURE

The two dolerite bosses stand up as steep-sided headlands and have served as a protection for the softer rocks behind them. At an earlier period there was probably a wide arm of the sea in the centre of the area, but, owing to the formation of the sand-spit, it has been filled up by alluvium. An exposure of solid rock occurs in the middle of this area and indicates that the river which rises in the S.W. flowed directly to the sea along the W. side of this exposure but has since been diverted owing to capture by the other stream. As pointed out above, the sand-spit has caused the main stream to flow westwards, parallel to the coast line and to enter the sea near the western headland.

The highest land is in the south of the area, in the region crossed by the trough of the syncline. The fault does not affect the topography.

g. GEOLOGICAL HISTORY

1. Formation of Ordovician series under marine conditions from mudstone to shale.

2. Uplift, folding and faulting, and erosion.

3. Intrusion of dolerite.

4. Area covered by ice-sheet and deposition of boulder clay.

5. Withdrawal of ice-sheet.

6. Formation of sand-spit, and deposition of alluvium.

7. Formation of river terrace. Further deposition of alluvium.

N.B.—Erosion has proceeded since the first uplift.

EXERCISES FOR THE STUDENT

Describe the geology of the country shown in Nos. 24, 25, 26, 27 and 29 in Platt's Series of Elementary Exercises and most of the maps from No. 5 onwards in Selected Exercises.

Map 9

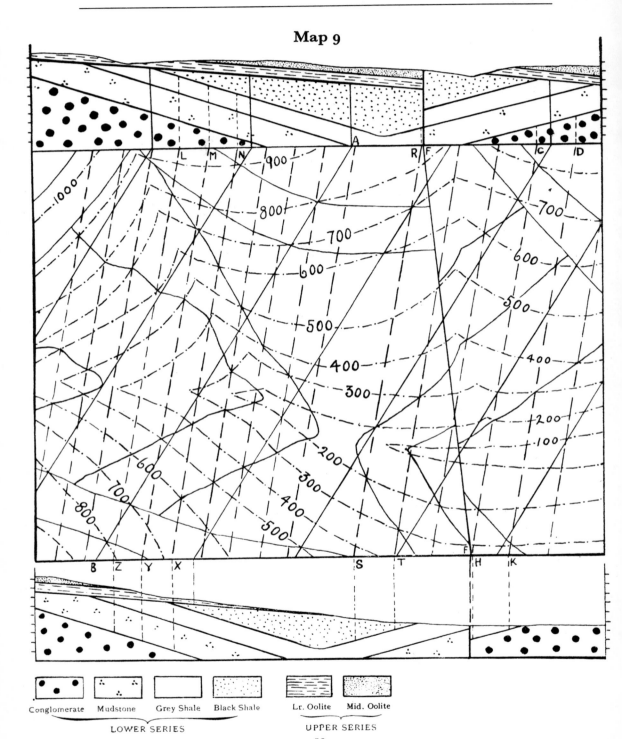

Conglomerate | Mudstone | Grey Shale | Black Shale | Lr. Oolite | Mid. Oolite

LOWER SERIES   UPPER SERIES

Map Exercise 9

CONSTRUCTION OF A MAP
FROM SECTIONS

[MAP 9]

PROBLEM   **Map 9 is a topographical map of an area. Geological sections are given along the northern and the southern edges. Complete the geological map of the area.**

[N.B.—To save printing two maps, the completed map is shown on the opposite page.]

Draw the altitude lines at 100 m intervals across the sections.

THE FAULT

The fault, being vertical, will be a straight line upon the map. It can, therefore, be mapped directly by projecting its outcrop in the sections on to the N. and S. edges of the map and joining the two points by the straight line FF.

THE UNCONFORMITY

The unconformity crosses the 700 m altitude line west of the fault in both sections.

Project these two points on to the N. and S. edges of the map at A and B respectively. Join AB. Then AB is the 700 m strike line for the unconformity. By projecting on to the respective lines of section the points where the unconformity crosses the other altitude lines, and drawing lines parallel to AB, other strike lines can be drawn at the following altitudes: 900, 800, 600 and 500 m on west of fault and at 700 m on east of fault. These lines have been drawn on the map. As this bedding plane has a constant dip, the interval between the strike lines is constant and, therefore, other strike lines can be drawn to cover the whole area.

Complete the outcrop of the unconformity on both sides of the fault as in map exercise 2. The outcrop has been drawn on the map.

THE BASE OF THE MIDDLE OOLITE

The lower Oolite is 100 m in vertical thickness throughout; therefore, the base of the middle Oolite has the same dip and strike as the unconformity, but the strike lines drawn on the map for the latter bedding plane will have new values, viz. each one will be 100 m higher.

53

Determine the values of the strike lines for the base of the middle Oolite and complete its outcrop on both sides of the fault. The outcrop has been drawn on the map.

THE LOWER SERIES

The rocks of the lower series maintain a constant strike throughout the whole area.

THE WESTERN LIMB OF THE SYNCLINE

The base of the grey shale crosses the 600, 500 and 400 m altitude lines in both sections.

Project these points on to the N. and S. edges of the map at L, M and N, and at Z, Y and X respectively. Join LZ, MY and NX. Then these lines are the 600, 500 and 400 m strike lines for the base of the grey shales. These lines have been drawn on the map as broken lines. Draw other necessary strike lines and complete the outcrop of the bedding plane.

The grey shales are 200 m in vertical thickness, therefore the outcrop of the base of the black shales can be completed by using the same strike lines but giving to them new values. Similarly, the outcrop of the base of the mudstone can be completed, for the mudstone is 300 m in vertical thickness.

THE EASTERN LIMB OF THE SYNCLINE

Strike lines CH and DK can be drawn as before for the base of the mudstone at 200 and 300 m, on the east side of the fault, and knowing these, the outcrop of the horizon can be completed. Similarly, the outcrops of the base of the grey shale and of the black shale can be completed for the eastern side of the fault. The outcrops on the western side of the fault can be completed by using the strike line RS, and the one parallel to it through T, which are the 200 and 300 m strike lines respectively for the base of the black shales.

EXERCISES FOR THE STUDENT

1. Give a full description of the geology of the area indicated on map 9.
2. Exercises 28a and 28b of Platt's Series (Elementary) are problems requiring the construction of geological maps from descriptions. These should present little difficulty if it is remembered to draw in the outcrops of the newest beds first and the oldest beds last.

Note 8

DESCRIPTION OF A GEOLOGICAL MAP

In writing a description of a geological map, it is advisable to deal with the points in a definite order.

The scheme given below is offered as one which includes all the points which usually occur in an elementary geological map and it has been followed in the descriptions given of maps 1, 3, 6, 7 and 8. It must be remembered that all the points do not occur in every map.

a. TABULATE THE SUCCESSION OF THE BEDS in the order of their relative ages, indicating the youngest and oldest beds. Group the beds into systems. If the beds are of constant thickness, give the value of the same (the vertical thickness is usually more easily determined).

b. STRUCTURE. Deal with the rock systems in turn, noting the following points (in the present work the newest system has always been taken first):

1. Dip of the beds (if not folded). Give direction and amount of dip and any variations in dip.

2. Folding. Give the following particulars of the folds: beds folded; nature and arrangement of folds; dips on the limbs (direction and amount); direction of axes of folding; and the age of the folding.

3. Faulting. If more than one fault, deal with each separately and state the type; inclination; direction; downthrow side; amount of vertical displacement; the age of faulting and the beds affected. If there are several faults comment on the relation between them.

4. Relation of folding and faulting.

c. RELATION OF ROCK GROUPS, i.e. position and nature of unconformities, etc.

d. IGNEOUS ROCKS. If more than one occurrence, deal with each separately and state the type (laccolite, dyke, sill, transgressive sill, flow, sheet, etc.), beds affected, age, etc.

e. SPECIAL POINTS, e.g. alluvium, raised beaches, river terraces, etc.

f. TOPOGRAPHY AND ITS RELATION TO THE GEOLOGICAL STRUCTURE

g. THE GEOLOGICAL HISTORY OF THE AREA

Note 9

DRAWING GEOLOGICAL SECTIONS

Details of the method of drawing geological sections for special cases have been given in exercises 1, 3, 5, 6, 7 and 8. It will only be necessary, therefore, to give here a few general rules of procedure.

THE LINE OF SECTION

The line of section should be chosen so as to show the arrangement of the rocks as fully and as clearly as possible.

A section drawn parallel to the dip of the most important series is essential and generally sufficient to give a clear idea of the structure of the area. The necessity for sections along other directions will depend upon special circumstances.

THE SECTION

Geological sections should be drawn to scale, i.e. the vertical scale used should be equal to the horizontal scale.

If the same scale as that of the map is adopted, a convenient way of transferring points is by using a strip of paper as described in exercise 3.

The profile must be drawn first.

Before filling in the section, determine the geological history of the area and then, in general, the section will be drawn in the reverse order to that in which the events occurred, e.g. see the order as given in map exercises 1, 3, 6, 7 and 8.

The position of the bedding planes must be determined by the use of strike lines. The alternative method of marking upon the profile the position of outcrop of the bedding planes and from these points drawing lines at the correct angles of dip, not only necessitates determining the values of apparent dips, but often leads to inaccuracy, for a slight error in the profile will cause a greater error in the position and thickness of the beds. There is no alternative, however, to this latter method in maps without contours (see map exercise 6). The strike line method has the further advantage of being a check upon the profile, for the outcrop of the beds in the section can always be tested and it may then be necessary to modify the profile, especially where the slopes are gentle and in consequence the contours widely spaced.

In folded series and in rocks with varying dip it must be remembered that the dip values refer only to the beds at the surface.

Indicate the different beds clearly in the section and, if possible, use the same stippling as on the map. Make stippling follow the bedding planes.

True thickness can only be measured directly from dip sections.